CHANG JIN-MING'S GUIDE TO REFEREEING STARE-OUT

CHANG JIN-MING

BLOOMSBURY

First published 2000
Copyright © Paul Hatcher 2000
www.house-of-hatch.com

The moral right of the author has been asserted

Bloomsbury Publishing Plc, 38 Soho Square, London W1V 5DF

A CIP catalogue record for this book
is available from the British Library

ISBN 0 7475 5219 3

10 9 8 7 6 5 4 3 2 1

Printed in Singapore by Tien Wah Press

CONTENTS

FOREWORD

When Chang told me that he had been commissioned to write a book about refereeing stare-out, I was tremendously excited! There is no other stare-out referee more qualified, more experienced and more respected than Chang. In fact many would argue that he's the best referee in the world!

Written in his engaging, chatty style, the book contains much useful information for players, officials and the casual reader alike. Over time, the book will no doubt prove an excellent reference book but there are also some insightful and often very funny anecdotes. Many people do not know that under Chang's officious exterior is a very humorous man - I'm sure that after he's hung up his stare-out whistle, a long career looms making after-dinner speeches!

Most books written about stare-out are dull, but this one isn't. I'm very happy to recommend this entertaining book to you.

Jacob Mycroberg

INTRODUCTION

Did you ever fancy yourself as the next Sigmund Spassky? Did you ever lie in bed dreaming of turning on some dazzling eyework and picking up the World Stare-out trophy?

You probably imagined yourself sitting at the stare table in North Park stadium in the warm afternoon sun, confidently drilling some acute glares at your opponent with over two hundred thousand fans tensely watching the furious contest. Suddenly you turn on the real style and there it is, you see the man opposite close his eyes!

The crowd goes berserk, and ringing in your ears is the chant of your name over and over, with people rushing up to you to congratulate you on your remarkable victory! Even your rival smiles and shakes your hand, congratulating you on the most incredible display of staring ever. Then you savour the lap of honour, waving at all the photographers and fending off kisses from hysterical fans. Finally you make you way up the famous twenty-one steps to the royal box, and adorned by hats and scarves bearing your national colours, you are at last handed the trophy by Her Royal Highness the Queen. You can't control your elation and peck her on the cheek before lifting the trophy to the watching world. The feeling of elation is one that will live with you forever. You are the best in the world. You are the World Stare-out Champion!

But then you wake up and realise that despite all your best efforts you can't stare to save your life. Perhaps your eyeballs seem to have a life of their own, refusing to stay open at the best of times, let alone in a stare-out match. Maybe your best stare-out efforts were subjected to the nastiest of ridicule by those more blessed in the eye department. Well who cares? Don't let that get you down - think positive and with just a few evening classes you could become an official stare-out referee!

Chang Jin-Ming
July 2000

Author's Note

The text uses male references only. This was mainly for ease of reading although the author respectfully acknowledges the huge strides being made by women in stare-out, both as players and as officials - long may it continue!

1

Development of the Game

The origin of stare-out is so interesting and glamorous that it deserves a whole book of its own, but we'll just make do with a quick summary here, touching on some of the historical background of staring.

The first known reference to staring was by the ancient Greek philosopher, Aristopolis, in his tract *Dialogues of Confrontational Philosophy.* Aristopolis describes the Sophists and philosophers trying to outdo each other with argument and also with what he called 'episkeptomai' or literally 'look at' (although 'examine' may be a more appropriate modern translation). Much historical speculation has been devoted to arguing whether or not the ancient Greeks specifically used staring as a sport, but there is no mention of stare-out in the ancient Olympic games. A common misconception is that stare-out originated in the Far East, because of how the ancient Japanese Samurai appear to be staring in Japanese art, but it is now thought that they were just trying to look tough.

In 15th century England, Charles David Orpington, the Third Earl of Skegness, famously referred to staring as 'a non-linguistic game'. He was widely known to enjoy indulging in a bit of psychological torture at parties -

indeed his friend Sir Percy Thornton wrote is his diary, 'Charles is a brilliant laugh at parties, staring out all the old dears!'. Many historical scholars

Greek vase c500BC: early evidence of stare-out
or pre-Socratic homo-erotic art?

consider Orpington to be the godfather of stare-out but although unquestionably a fierce dazzler with the eyes, he never had the opposition to play competitive stare-out.

Charles David Orpington 1480 (Detail): just look at the size of those pupils!

It may come as no surprise that it was the English who officially invented the game. Anthony Barrack-Smith is largely credited as being the man who devised the first crude stare-out laws whilst reading Media Studies at Keeble College, Oxford in 1850. Later that year he formed the All England School of Stare-out. At this stage in its development the game was played without any referees or match officials as the English tradition of good sportsmanship was thought enough to ensure that fair play was observed at all times. Any disputes or points of contention in the matches were settled amicably and the games always ended not only with a blink but also with a firm handshake and everybody had a good time. The game was then called 'gentlemen's stare-out' and was played in top hats and bow ties!

Refereeing was introduced to stare-out two years later when the sport came under the full glare of the media spotlight, for all the wrong reasons! In 1853

Gentlemen's stare-out became very popular in local taverns in the late 1880s. Note the use of tobacco by the player on the right.

Samuel Giles Benson was caught cheating in a university league match and was immediately suspended by the All England School. The disgrace that he brought on himself and Kings College meant expulsion from the league and from the university. By today's standards he would probably have received a minor suspension, but he never stared again. Ironically this fraudulent and scandalous behaviour did much to raise the profile of this emerging sport. A further scandal broke when it was discovered that Benson was working class.

Over the next few years the game was to grow nationally with the first Inter-county Stare-out Championship taking place in 1859 with one referee and a banquet table over forty-two feet long! The first stare-out league was formed and by 1870 there were five divisions, although the game was still amateur. It is widely believed that Otto Von Bismarck, the Prussian 'Iron' Chancellor, was a keen fan of stare-out. After discovering the sport on a visit to England, he challenged a French diplomat to a match. Bismarck was a notoriously bad loser and Prussia invaded France.

Minor leagues began appearing up and down the country and match attendances rose steadily, but by the turn of the century stare-out was still a minor event on the sporting calendar. It became very popular in England between the wars, with the first professional game taking place in 1932. By 1947 the International Stare-out Federation (ISF) was set up to deal with the growing administration that the game demanded, as international leagues and tournaments began springing up all over Europe. By now a top-level professional stare-master could just about earn a decent living.

In 1949 internal political infighting saw the ISF split into the World Stare-out Association (WSA) and the Alliance of Professional Stare-out (APS). The English remnant of the ISF became the Tyne and Wear Transport Workers Stare-out Division and League (TWTWSDL), quickly changing to the North England Club (NEC). The rise in television ownership in the fifties started to give stare-out a broader appeal which was the impetus it needed to become the sport it is today. Thankfully, to prevent the viewers becoming too confused, the WSA incorporated the ISF after the 1952 unifying stare-out final between the late great Dane, Thomas 'Mortar' Nielson and the American, Bobby 'Sandbag' Friedman. Nielson became the first undisputed World Stare-out Champion.

Today the WSA still has strong control over the game from organising tournaments to appointing new venues, and stare-out is more popular than ever. In England alone, there are over 8,500 affiliated clubs and over 28,000 unaffiliated clubs who won't pay their fees.

Sadly, England itself is no longer the world power in stare-out that it once was. This is mainly due to cuts in educational funding which has meant that many schools can no longer afford the facilities to play stare-out and nurture young stare-masters. However, as far as stare-out refereeing is concerned, England is still the pinnacle of excellence.

2

Becoming a Stare-out Referee

If you are already a budding stare-out player, learning to referee could add another string to your bow. Did you know that you can start to learn to ref at fourteen? The exceptional Chilean referee Eduardo Noriega is only twenty-nine and is the youngest man ever to referee a world quarter-final and he started in his mid teens - for young readers, that could be you! Personally, if I could have my time all over again, I would have started to learn about stare-out refereeing at as young an age as possible. I was a late starter, which is something I regret. I realised at the age of thirty-two that I would never make the grade as a professional stare-master but then I stumbled across an article about stare-out refereeing in a newspaper. It struck me as an interesting job and something I hadn't considered at all up to that point, so I immediately registered on a series of courses at the stare-out referees' official training school in Spalding.

With retirement from top-level refereeing compulsory at sixty, it is essential to start refereeing as early as possible, particularly if you have ambitions to climb to the top of the referees ladder. If you are not a career referee, there are still many other benefits to be had from joining the local branch of your Stare-out Referees' Federation - it could give you a very active social life! You can go

School of Stare-out Refereeing, Spalding

EXAMINATION FOR OFFICIAL STARE OUT REFEREE QUALIFICATION

For the following qualifications

Referee Class IV and B.Sc in Sports Science

COURSE CODE: STARER160

TITLE OF EXAMINATION: B.Sc Sport Science B160: Stare Out Referee

UNIT VALUE: 0.50

DATE: 10-MAY-00

TIME: 14.30

TIME ALLOWED: 1 hour 30 minutes

Answer all three questions.

The use of electronic calculators and geometry sets is permitted.
Graph paper, rulers and pencils will be provided on request.

1. List with full examples all events when the referee should use their whistle
during a stare out match. References to previous WSA ompetition matches and
controversial decisions will be rewarded.
[30 marks]

2.Either:
Describe the layout, as completely as possible, of a professional stare out
match. Use the graph paper provided to draw the relevant diagrams and ensure
that all measurements are given in metres.
[30 marks]
  Or:
Explain fully how and why the DeKaan rules for one-eyed stare out competitions
differ from official WSA rules.
[30 marks]

3. Give a complete chronological account of how a referee prepares for a match
starting from 24 hours before. Individual initiative will be rewarded.
[30 marks]

[10 marks will be awarded for correct grammar and presentation of papers]

END OF PAPER

to meetings to debate the latest changes in the laws of the game (it's vital to keep up with the current trends in stare-out) or discuss other referees' problems; there are dinner dances to attend and other social get-togethers. Or perhaps you would meet someone famous! Last year the East Cobham branch of the Referees' Federation managed to organise a charity dinner with guest speaker, media baron David Sullivan, a very keen stare-out ref! There's even more to think about; all that fresh air and exercise as well as the enormous opportunities to meet new people and make new friends!

But however serious you are about refereeing stare-out your local Referee Federation is always on hand to give you support and advice over any worries or concerns you may have about stare-out and stare-out refereeing.

So why not consider refereeing? There's no reason why a young boy or girl shouldn't want to be the next Dr Daniel Scanlon instead of the next Sigmund Spassky!

3

Stare-out Refereeing: The Essentials

Hopefully by now you will really want to be stare-out referee! The first thing that you'll need to do is get familiar with some of the detailed rules of the sport. If you are already a fan, then you will probably already know a fair bit about the game. Other good starting points are to chat with any referees that you may know and pick their brains. Find out how they got into refereeing and try to find out what makes them tick.

Courses

Register on any courses you can. Local colleges may offer evening classes in refereeing stare-out, so check out the local papers or one of the official gazettes, such as *Here's Looking at You*. If you can attend with a friend you can test each other at the end of each evening. This will help both of you to remember all the knowledge you have received. The evening classes usually run in six to eight week terms for a couple of hours a week, so there is a lot of learning to be done outside the classroom. The more you put in the more you get out. Depending on your age you can apply after just two of these courses as a class 1 referee. If you are between fourteen and eighteen-years-old then it is always best to choose a junior stare-out league younger than yourself. Kids can be difficult to handle, but in my experience it's the parents that can be the main problem! Many local councils run 'Stare-out in the community' schemes which often have ties with your local Referees' Association - look in the telephone directory for more information.

Equipment

There are some essential items of clothing and equipment: a black suit and tie and some nicely polished black shoes. You'll also need a pencil, a whistle, a watch, a coin and a notebook. There are a couple of other items that I always carry round with me, the first being a clean handkerchief just in case an insect lands in a player's eye and needs fishing out (this is especially important at junior level). The second item is some toilet tissue. I can remember one time when I was down to referee an inter-garage game in the West Midlands Passenger Transport League. I had just changed and was exercising my practise of going to the toilet before the match when I realised there was no toilet tissue. Learn from your mistakes!

Like the players you also need good eyesight. In the modern game match officials are allowed some forms of corrective spectacles, as it goes without saying that you need to be able to see what is going on and keep up with the play.

Presentation

I cannot stress how important personal presentation is. A stare-out referee at any level has to gain the respect of all the players and officials and he will not do so if he looks like Worzel Gummidge. Stare-out referees must always remember that they are marked out of ten by the players, managers and coaches. These marks are based on performances, personality and presentation. So you are being scrutinised before you even blow your whistle! These scores are sent in to the Referees' Association and are taken into consideration for future applications to higher refereeing positions. Most leagues offer a special cup to the best referee with the most points and the standard can be very high! I'm very proud to have won the Sir Sidney Lawrence Cup for refereeing excellence six times - a great achievement.

It is so important to create a good impression. Trousers should be pressed, shirts ironed, hair cut neatly etc. If you look good you will perform well and command the respect of the players. Many years ago I was involved in some stare-out coaching at the local primary school. Our school had a cup fixture with a rival school and twelve matches were to be played. I was sorting out the chairs and tables for the games when I was tapped on the shoulder.

''Scuse me mate, know where the bogs are?'

I turned round and saw the scruffiest looking person I had ever seen and immediately thought that the school had an unwanted intruder on the premises. But no, unbelievably this was today's match referee! I pointed him down the hall and told him that he could change in the staff cloakroom.

'Change? Oh it's alright, I'm reffing like this,' he muttered, puffing on his roll-up.

'Surely your aren't going out to referee twelve youth stare-out matches

The model referee should wear a black suit like the one shown.
I find Armani is always best.

dressed like that?' I gasped in amazement. 'What sort of example are you setting for the young children?'

'C'mon mate, it's not as if it's the world final or anything.'

I deplore this kind of attitude in stare-out. It is precisely this sort of lazy approach that has done much to undermine the progress of many young stare-masters.

'If I can give you a little bit of advice, I'd at least have a shave to indicate that you are showing an interest,' I said, wanting to knock some sense into his tiny little brain.

Of course, he chose to completely ignore my advice and he was diabolical. It was the worst case of stare-out refereeing incompetence I have ever seen. Our school lost the bout because that referee got so many decisions wrong and missed so many incidents. Some of the children's dads got so angry they left the school grounds before the final presentation. As it was I could only award him two points out of ten and I felt obliged to send in a full written report to the Referees' Association. I can only speculate that I may not have been the only coach to do such a radical thing, because one thing is for sure, I never saw that referee again. If only he had taken the advice from someone far more knowledgeable about the game.

4

Starting to Referee: Junior Level

The key to refereeing any stare-out match is preparation and there are some basics that you should always check before any match. First, always examine the table and chairs and ensure that they meet with WSA regulations for size and height etc. Make sure they do not wobble - there is nothing worse than a stare-out match on a table that keeps moving. It is good practice to get the players to agree that the table and chairs are acceptable. Also check the lighting - a fluorescent tube flickering halfway through the match is potentially harmful! Although you will be refereeing at youth level to begin with, these checks apply to any level of the game.

Many parents offer to be a second referee and although this is usually well intentioned I always avoid accepting the offer and I would advise you to do the same. Stare-out is a game of passion even when played by nine-year-olds and it is always difficult for someone to be completely impartial - except for fully trained referees like myself! A parent may feel the temptation to allow the game to develop in a way which may be contrary to fairness, or worse, they may want to take over altogether. In this case, one pair of eyes is definitely better than two. I would like to stress that it is very rare that a parent would be

The stare-out discipline began being taught in private schools in England around the turn of the century. The Marlton Boy's Stare-out team from 1920 was legendary although all of the players pictured here went on to become politicians.

cheating for his son but these situations are best avoided altogether.

There is a lot to think about when you first start to referee at the junior level and many children may cotton on to this. If some young boy realises you are a new referee they may try to soften you up by asking you some tough questions about the rules of stare-out, so be on your toes and make sure you know your stuff. Remember, you are the arbitrator, controller and adjudicator rolled into one - your duty is to enforce the laws and ensure sensible competitive play. A successful referee cannot succeed by innate skill and confidence alone - it requires hard graft and study too!

At the start of each game the children should shake hands, but often they will refuse. There is nothing in the rules that insists players should shake

Junior stare-out provides an ideal introduction for the novice referee, yet the problems faced can be as demanding as the professional game!

hands so just let it be, but be on your guard for a bad-tempered match. Junior games are usually limited to about five minutes or so but remember - watch the play at all times!

Once the game is underway, keep your eyes on the match - but be aware of what is going on around you. Off the table coaching is not allowed and at junior level parents often get over-excited and try to feed their son a few tips. The rules state that once play has started this is not allowed. However, after play has finished, I often explain to a young starer where they went wrong by means of a quick demonstration. This is to correct poor styles of play, as I am a firm believer in preventing bad technique at an early age. Sadly there are parents

Lloyd Obidiah (above left) could have chosen to play cricket, basketball or football as a junior player but elected to represent Jamaica at stare-out. Playing in his first professional match against Alessandro Kampagnola (below right) and making a social point.

who don't quite see this and voice their objections indiscreetly, 'They're only kids and you're spoiling it! Let them play their own game ref!'

Usually I respond politely by saying, 'I am doing my best to help these young players and would appreciate your support in allowing me to do this. Thank you.'

With due respect to any parents who think this advice is misguided, the young stare-masters of tomorrow want to learn techniques in the correct manner, and far from lessening their enjoyment of the game, my comments enhance it. As a referee you will learn how to deal with overzealous spectators.

It is critical that you never touch any player at any age but particularly at youth level. I knew a referee who got so frustrated with a ten-year-old boy's constant flouting of the rules that he gave the young boy a quick shake. Unfortunately the young man's father saw what had happened and the referee ended up involved in an altercation to which the police were called. To make matters worse, the Referees' Association suspended the referee.

5

The Amateur Game

In the amateur game (or 'semi-professional' as it is now known), you will be expected to referee for up to an hour maximum with a two minute stare-break halfway through the game, and it is here that you will need to rely on a second official - the match timekeeper. The timekeeper's role is to sound the buzzer to ensure that the official stare-break occurs and the partition board is in place

COMPETITION			DATE	TIME
PLAYERS				
COLOUR OF EYES				
INCIDENTS				
TALKING				
SWEATING				
MOVING				
SWALLOWING				
DISSENT				
CAUTIONS				
DISMISSAL				
RESULT			DURATION	
TABLE/LIGHT			DR ON DUTY	
MATCH OFFICIALS (Signature and name)				

An example of a clean playing card.

for the full two minute duration.

Refereeing with a timekeeper should make your life easier, but make sure that you don't saddle the timekeeper with responsibility he cannot cope with. Often the timekeeper is a fully trained referee who may feel aggrieved at the lesser role in the game, so try to maintain a good relationship with him and be sure to clarify his role before the match to avoid any problems. Timekeepers sometimes feel left out of the action so it is always a good idea to acknowledge any comments or remarks he makes - I occasionally consult the timekeeper for a second opinion on something even if I have already made my mind up. Failing to acknowledge a timekeeper can lead to him to become demoralised and he may lose interest in the game.

It is vital to keep your playing card filled in throughout the game, as the match may go the distance and will need to be settled by a points decision given by the referee. Mark the players on their composure, posture, any signs of sweating or flickering eyes, excessive movement, nervous swallows etc. It can be a contentious issue when deciding the winner of the match by a points decision. In fact, referees' decisions have occasionally sparked off some ugly scenes.

Points wins are not a science, but good judgement is vital if both players blink simultaneously and the match is a dead heat. Thankfully this is very rare, but it is here that the second official can play an important role in assisting you. Try not to let the second official undermine your authority or be afraid that they will laugh at your mistakes - every top referee has made errors of one sort or another, perhaps miles worse than any you have made! We all make incorrect decisions now and again, so bear in mind that you are in good company when you blunder.

I was once refereeing a Southern England Fire Brigade Division 2 match, when I briefly turned away from the action as my coat had got stuck under my chair. I immediately heard a huge cheer and I realised that I had missed something on the stare-table. I asked the official timekeeper what had happened but he refused to co-operate saying, 'You're today's referee, you tell me'. The crowd was shouting and as I looked at the table I could see one of the players with a sheepish look on his face and the other with a big broad grin. Although I hadn't seen anything I knew that something had happened.

COMPETITION	Andorra Masters		DATE 10/6/99	TIME 14-00
PLAYERS	Rudolph Breffen (GER)		Reubens Roomie (MEX)	
COLOUR OF EYES	GREEN (LL) BROWN (R)		Brown Green	Blue
TALKING	1	15-20	0	
SWEATING	0		1	15-20
MOVING	0		1	15-19
SWALLOWING	C		1	15-19
DISSENT	1	15-21	0	
CAUTIONS	1	16-22	0	
DISMISSAL	0		0	
RESULT	1		0	
LIGHT	GOOD		DURATION	1h 23m
TABLE	SOLID		DR ON DUTY	Dr. Sick
MATCH OFFICIALS				

An example of a completed playing card.

'Stare on, I didn't see anything!' I shouted.

It is essential that you never try to guess decisions. The game continued for a few minutes and then the player who had been smiling, blinked, and the game was over. Full credit had to go to both players for staring to the whistle! I then asked one of the spectators what had happened and was told that I had missed a stare-out against the man to whom I had just awarded victory.

I knew that I had dropped a clanger of the greatest magnitude.

After I had changed out of my referee's suit, I went to the changing room of the player who had lost. The player and his coach were furiously discussing the game. I knocked and entered, and explained what had happened and apologised to all involved.

'If it makes any difference to you, I promise never to make the same mistake again,' I said.

The player and coach were both nice.

'Don't worry about it ref - it was good of you to come over and apologise, we all make mistakes and we're all human!'

I was very pleased that they were so good about it - in fact we struck up a good relationship and became friends.

This incident shows the merit in honesty, integrity and sometimes a bit of humility - all qualities that a stare-out ref should possess. People are more forgiving than you would think and have a lot of respect for an official who can admit to being wrong.

But it didn't end there. I was very disappointed at not getting the respect and support that I deserved from the official timekeeper, who could have easily

The mechanical stare-break (above) implemented as a safety precaution to amateur players, and Dr Daniel Scanlon (left) practising his manual stare-break technique.

Stare-out is a game and is meant to be enjoyed. Referees should have a good sense of humour and enjoy the game and help others to enjoy it too.

My first professional match as referee featured the two great Russian innovators, Ivan Chevkesky (left) and Mitchell Pavlov (right). The match itself proved to be a rather uneventful, grey-suited affair.

The great Spassky v Uzlian championship decider was my first world final as match referee. Spassky was a virtual unknown then but he rocked the world of stare-out, thrashing Uzlian, in a match that is still referred to as 'The Spassky Final'.

'They don't come much braver than Jurgen Ziege.' Everyone will remember Jurgen Ziege's match during the German Open qualifiers, when he defeated the Paraguayan Jose Luis Gamarra despite playing the whole match with a broken arm. There was much controversy that I allowed the match to start but my judgement was correct.

Advances in technology have made decision making easier for referees. It also brings the fans closer to the action regardless of the scale of the event, which makes stare-out even more exciting!

Always keep your head when others are losing theirs...As a referee you are responsible for overseeing fair play so don't stand for any nonsense!

The disorder seen at Bremmen Heights stadium (above) was one of the darkest days in world stare-out. The resulting Epson enquiry fully exonerated my decision to allow the match to continue in the hope that the action would settle the hooligans down to watch the match, thus preventing a minor scuffle descending into a full scale riot.

Expecting the unexpected doesn't come any more unexpected than this! Argentinian Parachutist Ariel Passarella (right) used the South American Cup match between Freddy Dario Gomez and Carlos Chivert as a stunt to promote his new sky-diving club. A remarkable incident that proves absolutely anything can happen in stare-out. I ordered the match to be restarted and Gomez won.

Daniel **Scanlon** | Chang **Jin-Ming** | Jacob **Mycroberg**

A Question of Stare-Out: the popular quiz game between the officials and players was as fiercely contested as any world stare-out match! The refs' side (above), captained by myself, just pipped the players (below) in the 'on the buzzer' round. I was particularly proud of recognising Roman Solowka as a baby in the first 'picture board' round.

Quincey **Sanders** | Sigmund **Spassky** | Dmitry **Starostin**

I was chosen to preside over Ted Stead's fantastic record breaking attempt for the longest period of time without blinking (above). The attempt was set under strict match conditions, but sadly had to be restarted after ten hours as a careless well-wisher used flash photography.

It is always a pleasure to referee Ted's matches, as he is one of the cleanest stare-masters in the game. He has never been cautioned and is a real gent.

The media profile expands the higher up the referees' ladder you climb. Here I am featuring in popular serial The Elipio Duarte *story from* Boys Own Comics. *There I am on right hand side of the fifth panel!*

resolved the situation with the minimum of fuss. The following week I was refereeing in the same league and the game's official timekeeper was the same man from the previous week. I decided I had no choice but to dismiss the man from his duties, as I had lost all confidence in him and I would feel undermined in the match - a situation that was clearly unacceptable. To my surprise, the official timekeeper voiced his opposition to my decision, in full view of the crowd and players. But I stood firm and insisted that he wasn't keeping time on this particular afternoon. As a referee, you are fully entitled to do this and take sole charge of the game. This sort of decision is never an easy one to make, but correct judgement and high standards on matters such as these mean you'll go far in stare-out refereeing.

6

Professional Stare-out

If you have made it to professional level then well done! Professional stare-out is the arena where every referee wants to officiate. You have no doubt studied hard for your exams and theory tests and most importantly refereed many matches. The fundamental basics of the professional game are the same, nevertheless the baffling technology can be a bit daunting to the newly qualified referee. But don't worry! You'll soon be fully competent at operating the surveillance and video equipment - particularly after a few Referees' Association courses.

The complexity of the top-level game means the pressure on the match officials is at its most intense, as is the high level of responsibility - responsibility that sorts out the greatest referees from the mere hobbyists! Today's referees are as important as the top players, as we have such an decisive role in the game. It is a great feeling knowing that you are in charge of a professional stare-out match and it gives me enormous satisfaction making correct decisions and refereeing well. I get a lot of pleasure from meeting world class champions, let alone being in charge of their matches! I've refereed the greats; players of such stature as Micheal Leguizamo, Illy

Amarlric, Fred Smith and Taki Tagmari - stare-masters who played such an integral part in making the modern game as popular as it is today. Some of these names may be unfamiliar to you but ask your granddad who they were and I'm sure he'll enjoy telling you about the exploits of these giant personalities in the game of stare-out.

The pre-match medical
Before the match all players have to undergo a series of medical tests on their eyes. This is part of the WSA action plan to stamp out the illegal use of drugs in the sport, and as the match referee you have to be present. Although controversial when it was first brought into effect, most players now happily realise the necessity of such regulations. They are subjected to a series of short tests where a medical eye specialist takes a sample tear from the eye as well as a urine sample. Red-eye is a possible indication of the use of illegal substances but can be due to over training or pre-match nerves so initial physical checks are by no means conclusive. It is a constant battle to keep up with the cheats in stare-out, due to the development of masking drugs which hide the effects of eyelid steroids strengthening the eye-lid muscles or keeping the pupil dilated in bright light. The Danish stare-master, Henning Bo-Larsen, is the biggest name to be disgraced as a result of the tests, after it was revealed that he had undergone surgery for eyeball enlargement.

Officials
At professional level you will be in charge of a team of four officials altogether,

but you are ultimately still the final decision-maker. A good team spirit is needed to ensure that mistakes are minimised. Unfortunately refereeing is like any position of authority and does attract those who have no interest in stare-out but simply like to boss people around; however, there is no room for this at the top level. The modern game has become faster and tactics are constantly developing, so you always need to be on your toes.

Weather
Outdoor stare-out gives the spectator the added excitement of the uncertainty of the weather, giving the game a dangerous edge. Many players prefer to play stare-out in certain conditions, for instance performing far better with a light westerly breeze over their shoulder. However, twelve years ago the WSA decreed that stare-out could no longer be played in serious adverse weather conditions after Jimmy 'Boy' Leyton and Akino 'Hari-scari' Kariarto were electrocuted and died whilst playing on a metal table in a fierce electrical storm. Inevitably metal chairs and tables were banned for good from the game, ensuring this tragedy would never be repeated. It also meant that a lot of the excitement was taken away from outdoor stare-out. It is your responsibility as the match referee to take the players off at the first sign of rain, although the groundsman will be responsible for placing the plastic tablecloth over the table and chairs. Bad light can also be a factor, although the increased use of floodlights for all night staring has reduced the need to take the players off. Be aware that some of your decisions could be unpopular with the crowd - but never let the reaction of the spectators affect your decision.

Hot weather: players are now allowed to have one drink every hour when the temperature on the stare-table is over 32 degrees centigrade. New Zealander Dill Stamm (left) uses sun block to prevent his nose getting burnt, although the WSA is currently looking into its use for intimidation purposes.

Examples of Playmanship. (clockwise from top left) Norman Farnsworth's infamous hand tatooes. Maverick Scottish staremaster John Doran producing finger puppets against Dutchman Guus Seedorf and more re-interpretation of the rules against Pakistan's Anand Nanak. Doran's antics have led to the WSA having to amend the rules no less than eleven times!

The other extremes of the weather can also be problematic. In the Indian Masters two years ago the heat on the stare-table reached a phenomenal 44 degrees centigrade - a real problem for the Icelandic Master, Jan 'Iceman' Tôrk, who collapsed with serious dehydration. Since that incident, in extreme conditions the players can bring a single water bottle with a straw and can get fresh water with a minimum of movement during the match. The glare of the sun used to be a concern but nowadays most professional stare-masters' eyes are so strong, sun-glare is rarely a problem.

Cynical Play

With hundreds of thousands of pounds resting on each blink, players will do anything to get any small advantage over their opponents. Always check that the player's clothes have no writing on them or any logos - no text on any shirt is allowed. When I first started to referee, players were constantly trying to push back the boundaries of what was allowed by wearing T-shirts with jokes written on them in an attempt to distract their opponents. Now a law has been brought in to prevent such playmanship. American Norman Farnsworth famously got round this ruling by tattooing on his knuckles 'YOUR'E DEAD!' [sic] in order to shock his opponent. He was later forced to have the text surgically removed.

One bit of pre-match controversy that I got caught up in was when I was refereeing the first round of Cadbury's Invitation Event between Frenchman Nathan 'Art' Le Bihan and American Bobby Lee 'Loop' Lloyd. Le Bihan had cleverly distributed thousands of enlarged photos of himself amongst his fans, which were then held up when his opponent entered the arena. The sight of thousands of Le Bihans upset the American, but I explained to him that it was all within the rules as long as they put them away at the start of play. Lloyd was thrashed inside three minutes and complained bitterly afterwards. Unfortunately Lloyd had to eventually be escorted away by the police, but I was congratulated by the WSA about the way I had handled this situation and the general manner in which I refereed the game.

With players interpreting the rules to their advantage, the referee must keep calm at all times and use his management skills effectively, so that trouble can be nipped in the bud. Failure to do this can lead to unwanted escalations. Always be firm and fair and remember that the thing to do is to avoid trouble before it begins, as prevention is better than cure. Minor villainy is usually manageable in this way, but the next chapter deals with foul play in more detail.

Injuries

Stare-out, like many sports, can be dangerous. Make sure that you stop the game if an injury has occurred but be aware of play-acting - some players may do this to break the concentration of their opponent. Occasionally some dust or grit may find its way into the eye of a player; be prepared to stop the game so that the player can be treated. Natural hazards such as insects are something to be wary of too. I remember well a South Nippon Cup match in which Japan's Koyanni Squatsi forced a win despite being stung on the eyeball by a wasp. A tremendous achievement, but sadly the after-effects ended Squatsi's career.

Crowd Interference

The spectators rarely interfere with play in any serious manner and the most that you will have to do is occasionally control the noise levels during moments of excitement. I find being polite, but to the point, very effective. 'Quiet please, ladies and gentlemen, the players are ready to stare, thank you,' usually does the job. However, with crowds of over 200,000 at each match it isn't realistic to expect total silence - especially if many units of alcohol have been consumed. Sadly, alcohol played a large part in the Bremmen Heights stadium disturbances involving English and German fans during the match between Mongolian Ky Jeet and Zimbabwe's Ollie Soont. The low police presence meant hundreds of thousands of pounds worth of damage as the crowds went on the rampage and neither myself nor any of my colleagues were in a position to contain the violence. The yearlong Epson enquiry that followed produced over seventy recommendations for the WSA to implement and now the police or stewards deal with any crowd problems. Old tricks like spectators trying to dazzle a player with the sun using a mirror, or the deliberate rustling of a newspaper, are now very rare too.

Stare-out

Ending a stare-out match is usually a straightforward affair, but inevitably there will come a time when the decision is anything but clear. As part of my referee training some years ago, I was watching a closely fought match between Maurice 'Paper' Ponsford and Wes 'Focal' Khan in the Korean Open. Naturally the weather was a feature of the game. Ponsford had clearly not

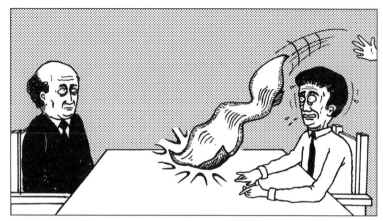

Always be aware of the towel being thrown in if a player is struggling, or be prepared to stop the match yourself if necessary. Coaches often come to the rescue of players that are struggling.

acclimatised well and was sweating profusely. Although he looked uncomfortable in the heat he seemed to be dictating the game with a volley of stubborn moves which were giving Khan difficulty. Khan's concentration was clearly wavering and the match seemed at last to be going Ponsford's way when the referee suddenly stepped in, and because Ponsford was sweating so much, he ended the contest awarding the match to Khan. The protests that followed were understandable, as the referee had prematurely concluded the match on the grounds that Ponsford was in such trouble. What the referee had failed to realise was that at twenty-seven stone Ponsford always sweats uncontrollably at the best of times, and the heat was making it worse. The result stood and Maurice Ponsford lost out. The referee was correct to be concerned but he had made an incorrect decision. This does serve to illustrate just how difficult making a decision can be. Often managers will see that their player is in deep trouble and throw in the towel. However, even this can bring controversy if the players want to stare-on. Remember, always act with confidence and have the courage of your convictions, as you may be required to make split-second decisions at critical moments in the match.

Whatever situations you find yourself in as a professional referee, do remember to have fun. Occasionally you have to remind yourself that stare-out is only a game and should be enjoyed by all concerned - players, officials and fans alike. Just think that refereeing world stare-out is still a piece of cake compared with doubles matches or tag team stare-out!

7

Foul Play

When the stakes are high and the pressure mounts, tempers can become frayed and so the role of the referee in maintaining correct play at all times, is imperative. The bottom line is that this is why we are entrusted with this job - to ensure that the rules are adhered to. The high amounts of money that are associated with stare-out inevitably attract some unwanted elements, such as the Far East betting syndicates that prey on young impressionable stare-masters, wanting them to throw a game for financial gain. There are many seedy aspects of bribery and corruption in the game. Last year saw the jailing of World Stare-out referee, Edin Dizdar, for trying to influence the outcome of a world championship quarter-final. Once a referee is corrupt then there is no stare-out.

Dealing with Dissent

Dissent in stare-out increases the further up the referee's ladder you climb. It is a sad fact that players and players' managers increasingly argue with the referee. If they are unhappy with an aspect of the game they seem only too ready to voice their concern. You have the skills and ability to deal with these situations in a mature and confident way. You don't have to put up with those whose opinions differ from the official one, but remember to deal with dissent in a way that dissipates any anger in the situation - sometimes you could be expected to stare-out a stare-master!

It is statistically proven that the less experienced referee is far more likely to encounter difficulties at a match and is less likely to spot trouble. Always try to dissipate any bad feeling between the players, by having quiet word before the match. Usually I find it sufficient to say something along the lines of: I know you both feel you have something to prove but do the right thing and show us what you've got with your

Disgraced: Edin Dizdar being led away by an officer of the law after being arrested during a world quarter-final, on corruption charges.

eyeballs. Players are not allowed to speak during the match and will be given up to three warnings before finding themselves dis-qualified. If a player does talk during a match there is no need to go overboard. A warning such as 'please stop talking' is fine. You have the power to dismiss the player if it gets out of hand and award the match to his opponent. Warn the player who has

Confrontation: sometimes you have to stare-out a stare-master. The picture shows me laying down the law to Russia's, Andre Hendicov. This image won photographer Larry Patterson, sports photo of the year.

transgressed that this is your intention and give him the chance to quieten down. Likewise, you can force the manager to watch the rest of the match from the stands if he is being a nuisance or engaging in anti-social antics. Try not to make the warning confrontational and threatening but say something like: I will award the match to your opponent if you don't stop arguing with me - I'm in charge here, not you, so carry on staring.

Never make idle threats to the players. If you can't enforce them, you will lose the respect of all concerned and become a bit of a joke.

On one occasion in the North American Open, Dr Roland Pill of Canada, coughed violently during a match. His opponent, Ireland's Seamus 'Cactus' Rafferty, accused Pill of deliberately coughing in his face in order to put him

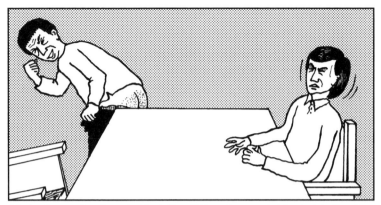

Bringing the game into disrepute: China's Xiang K. Cheng in an over-indulgent celebration after his first world quarter-final victory. It cost him a £100 fine and the tabloid press had a field day.

off his staring. Subsequent TV replays were inconclusive and I felt that Pill had to be given the benefit of the doubt. Alas, Pill coughed again and this time a tiny particle of spittle landed on the nose of Rafferty. Pill immediately apologised. I thought this was obviously accidental and told both players to play on. Unfortunately Rafferty then lost his temper and screamed that I was 'too old to referee'. Even after I handed him an official warning he carried on arguing. After a fierce confrontation I had no alternative but to send Rafferty from the table and hand the game to Pill. It was one of the most heart-stopping moments of my career. Afterwards I received full backing from the WSA and Rafferty was suspended for three months for 'conduct unbecoming of a professional stare-master'.

Violent Conduct

Although serious foul play in stare-out has increased, it is thankfully still rare. Needless to say stare-out is a non-contact sport - indeed any physical contact between the players, above and below the table, is not allowed. Certain players, such as Ireland's Seamus 'Cactus' Rafferty and Tibet's Orgyen 'Rudder' Chokling, have had previous for violent conduct, drug taking and other offences, so you need to be aware of this and watch them with a keen eye. This

Under attack: Crazed fan Annabel Long attacks Norway's Peter 'Blade' Florquest during his match against Thomas 'T.B.' Bjurefelt. Dr Daniel Scanlon bravely restrained her and it transpired that she was infatuated with Bjurefelt and wanted to marry him.

is a shame as they are such superb starers. The press core will often try and stir up some tension at the pre-match press conference and any rivalry whipped up there between the players, may spill out on the stare-table.

Regardless of the levels of passion and intensity of the match, all cases of spitting, table-tapping, abusive language, obscene gestures, exposing oneself and head-butting are instantly dismissable offences. Remain firm and assertive, but remember to treat the players with respect, as a sending off is after all one of the most embarrassing moments of a player's career and it is taking place in front of a big crowd and probably a large audience on television too. Once a player has been removed from the stare-table the match is over and you must now do your duty and file your report with unforgiving authority. Take the player's name and write down details of what the incident was and at what point of the match it occurred. Make sure you check your spelling and grammar - irrespective of the unpleasantness of the task you must always make yourself look good. The report must be submitted to the WSA within two weeks, so make sure you use a first-class stamp.

Threats to Referees

If you are ever approached in a menacing fashion, then try to deal with it using all your diffusing skills outlined in your training, but remember not to overreact! Most referees take it as read that they will be jostled at least a couple of times in their career as read - indeed Dr Daniel Scanlon once had a trainer's bucket bounced off his head! But where would the game be without a bit of red-blooded excitement every now and then? I am not condoning this sort of behaviour, as it is of course disgraceful and none of us wish to see this sort of thing in stare-out.

Assaults on referees are still reassuringly rare and there is a procedure to follow in the most unlikeliest of events:

1 Abandon the game if still being played (your safety is more important than a stare-out match).
2 Ask around for witnesses in case of a criminal action - I find most decent people are only too willing to assist in the upholding of the law.
3 Notify the local constabulary - many off-duty police officers love stare-out so don't be surprised if you are approached by a helpful off-duty bobby.
4 Report it by phone and by letter to the WSA.
5 Speak to someone. You may need counselling.

I must stress again that this really is an exceptional occurrence and in my nineteen years of refereeing I have never once had a problem - although as a junior coach I did witness a minor assault at a junior inter-county schools' match. The match referee that day asked a young boy to take out his bubblegum before the match, as is standard procedure - but the lad's father took exception to his son being made an example of and punched the ref, knocking out his two front teeth and breaking his jaw. More widely known is the tragic case of Augulio Perentis who made a controversial decision in the final of the South American Cup which resulted in Chile winning the trophy against

Columbia. He was shot dead two hours after the end of the match. It is a very sad fact that the shooting of Perentis resulted in the number of applications to become a stare-out referee dropping significantly around the world.

Augulio Perentis: Shortly before being shot dead by a lone gunman.

8

Percy Starling: Post-war Great

Percy Starling was one of the all-time great pre-war stare-masters. Like many men of his generation, World War II rudely interrupted his career in 1939. Percy was drafted and proved himself a natural lookout for the Royal Infantry's 2nd Battalion. He received many medals and commendations for bravery before returning to England after being hit in the shoulder by a German sniper.

After the war Percy returned to his hometown of Hull, knowing any serious chances of competing at the top level of stare-out had gone - his shoulder injury meant that he couldn't maintain the sitting position that had terrorised so many players before the war. After briefly resuming his original career as a funeral director, he began a 'Sports Tactics and the Psychology of Winning' evening class at his local college and then registered as a stare-out referee two months later.

By 1948 he was refereeing Saturday afternoon matches regularly and as resources were still scarce in post-war Britain, Percy proudly dressed in his old funeral suit. His progress was such that he became one of the most widely known and highly regarded referees in the prestigious East Yorkshire League. His reputation grew and he became known as 'the fairest man in black'.

Percy Starling (centre) proudly conducts the official handshake before the 1952 unifying match between Dane Thomas 'Mortar' Neilson (left) and American Bobby 'Sandbag' Friedman (right).

In 1950 Percy led the first team of referees and officials in the Pan European Union League as well as taking his place as an advisor to the then fractious International Stare-out Federation. It came as no surprise when Percy was chosen to referee the famous 1952 unification match between Nielson and

Friedman. Percy did a superb job under enormous media pressure, not putting a foot wrong, thereby being instrumental in ensuring that the unification went smoothly.

The following year, Percy retired from refereeing as his shoulder was now so painful that he couldn't manage the sheer physical exertion of refereeing stare-out. It is interesting to note the favourable profile Percy gave to refereeing - his home town of Hull went on to produce a number of top referees such as Ned Bigger, Arthur Harry, Sid Bliss and Jack Poppett to name just a few. All these men agreed that they would never have taken up the whistle without Percy's influence.

In 1954, following retirement, Percy was given the OBE by HM The Queen for services to stare-out and was then given freedom of the City of Hull in the same year. During his retirement, Percy wrote prolifically on stare-out, including several books on the game: *Opening Repertoire for Attacking Players* (1954); *40 Lessons for the Club Player* (1955); *Think like a Stare-master* (1955); *Test Your Tactical Ability* (1955) and *Test Your End-game Ability* (1955). He died in 1956, leaving his last book - *Secrets of Stare-mastery*, unfinished.

9

The Lighter Side of Stare-out

I am very proud to be part of a game that has touched so many people and is such an important part of their lives. This wonderful sport has given me so much enjoyment over the years and will, I'm sure, continue to do so. As well as the serious business of officiating matches there is a lighter side of being a top-level referee that is just as rewarding.

Sigmund Spassky, generously donating his time to the children of Gdansk.

Roman Solowka's testimonial match was a pleasure to referee except for the suppressed rage of Seamus Rafferty, which spoilt the occasion somewhat.

One of the things that I always try to remember about the highest paid stare-masters in the world is their unwavering support of charities and the amount of hard work they put in to raise money for good causes. It is wonderful to be able to be involved in charity stare-a-thons, pro-celebrity stare-out, and the wonderfully entertaining exhibition matches. I particularly marvel at the hard work world champion Sigmund Spassky does, at his annual charity stare-out for the Great Olanov Eye Hospital in his hometown of Gdansk. Sitting all day whilst young fans attempt to stare him out, raises about £1,500,000 for this wonderful cause. What a thrill it must be for young boys (and girls!) to not only meet their idol, but also to play against him - albeit for about two seconds or so which is about as long as they last.

I'm always very happy to be involved in charity work and it was great that I was the match official when Ted 'The Head' Stead smashed the record for not blinking for two days three hours and twenty-three seconds, raising an amazing £3,500,000 for the Texas State Penitentiary rehabilitation programme.

I would really recommend that you get involved in as many of these events as you can, as it will raise your profile as a referee and raise some money for charity too. There are plenty of opportunities in stare-out and they are all great fun. Exhibition matches mean that the players are relaxed and can talk through their techniques, demonstrating what real showmen they are. I particularly enjoy testimonial matches and was thrilled to be asked along to officiate at the last match of one of the greats, Roman 'The Doorman' Solowka. Everyone gave the Ukrainian a lovely send-off. Pro-celebrity stare-out is also great fun although you'll be amazed at how intense it can get. Entertainer Les Dennis is extremely competitive and takes his stare-out very seriously.

It was also a very proud moment to be the first referee in any sport to record a world stare-out single *Play It Fair*. The producers used my own lyrics on the record which was a real thrill, and it reached number 104 in the soul/funk charts. I've also appeared on many chat shows and even in a couple of Christmas pantomimes. So get involved and remember, above all, have fun!

Acknowledgements

Chang Jin-Ming would like to thank:

Pro-Look Clothes Ltd; West Barrow Stare-out & Health Club; Adrian Sellers of Eyes Open: The Stare-out Specialists of Bond Street, London; Devon Lilt and Stella Bucks; Kasper de Graaf and the Museum of Stare-out in Amsterdam; Bob Goodnut and Craig McCutt for advice and criticism; William Webb; Mike Jones; Polly Napper; Jo Vaughan and Sarah Wicks of The Stare-out Memorabilia Club; The Stare-out Picture Library; Don Wendy; Ian Brown; Chris Shepherd; Angela Malin and Andrew Wintersgill; Dan Bartlett; Doug McKenna; Nick Dimmock; T G Hatcher; Chris Pound and my long suffering wife Norma.

The Elipio Duarte Story reproduced courtesy of Boys Own Comics. Published by 5 x 5 Ltd. Used with permission.

About the Author

Chang Jin-Ming has been refereeing stare-out for nineteen years. He has recently been accepted into the Guild of Stare-out Referees and now is a WSA Licensed Instructor of Referees. He is also a technical consultant for the new Hollywood stare-out film, *Escape to Victory II*.

Chang's first book, *The Top 100 Games of Sigmund Spassky* was a best-seller. He works as a part-time social worker and lives in Milton Keynes with his wife.